relaxation

the ultimate piano chillout selection

FABER *ff* MUSIC

Faber Music in association with Classic FM, a Global Radio station.
Faber Music is the exclusive print publisher for all Global Radio sheet music product.

© 2012 Faber Music Ltd
First published in 2012 by Faber Music Ltd
Bloomsbury House
74–77 Great Russell Street
London WC1B 3DA
Music processed by Jeanne Roberts
Cover design by Susan Clarke
Printed in England by Caligraving Ltd
All rights reserved

ISBN10: 0-571-53613-1
EAN13: 978-0-571-53613-9

To buy Faber Music/Global Radio publications, or to find out about the full range of titles available,
please contact your local retailer, or go to www.fabermusic.com or www.classicfm.com/shop.
For sales enquiries, contact Faber Music at sales@fabermusic.com or tel: +44(0)1279 828982.

Contents

Gymnopédie No.1

Erik Satie

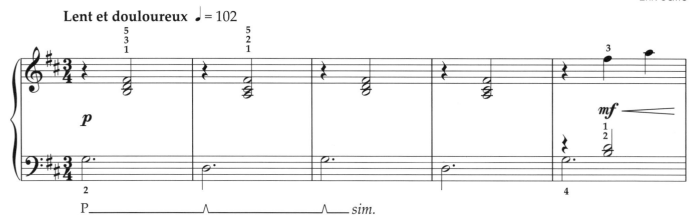

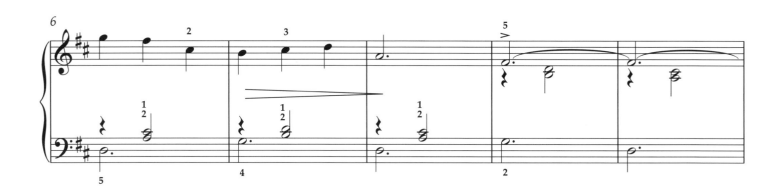

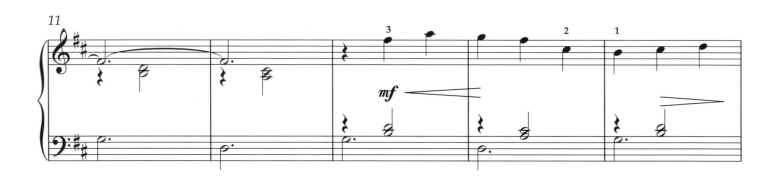

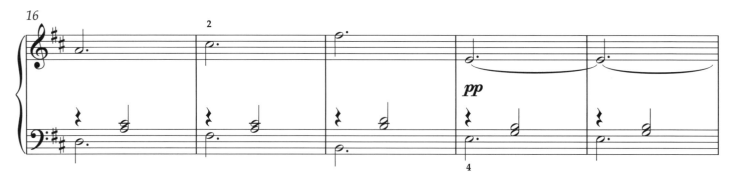

2nd time to Coda ⊕

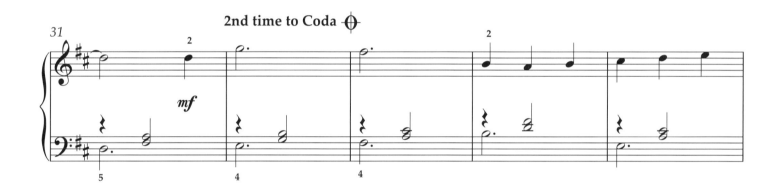

poco rit.   D. C. al Coda   CODA

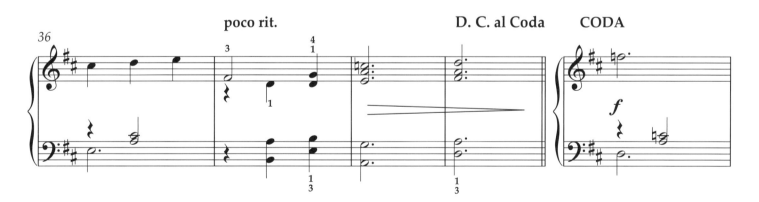

poco rit.

Vladimir's Blues

Max Richter

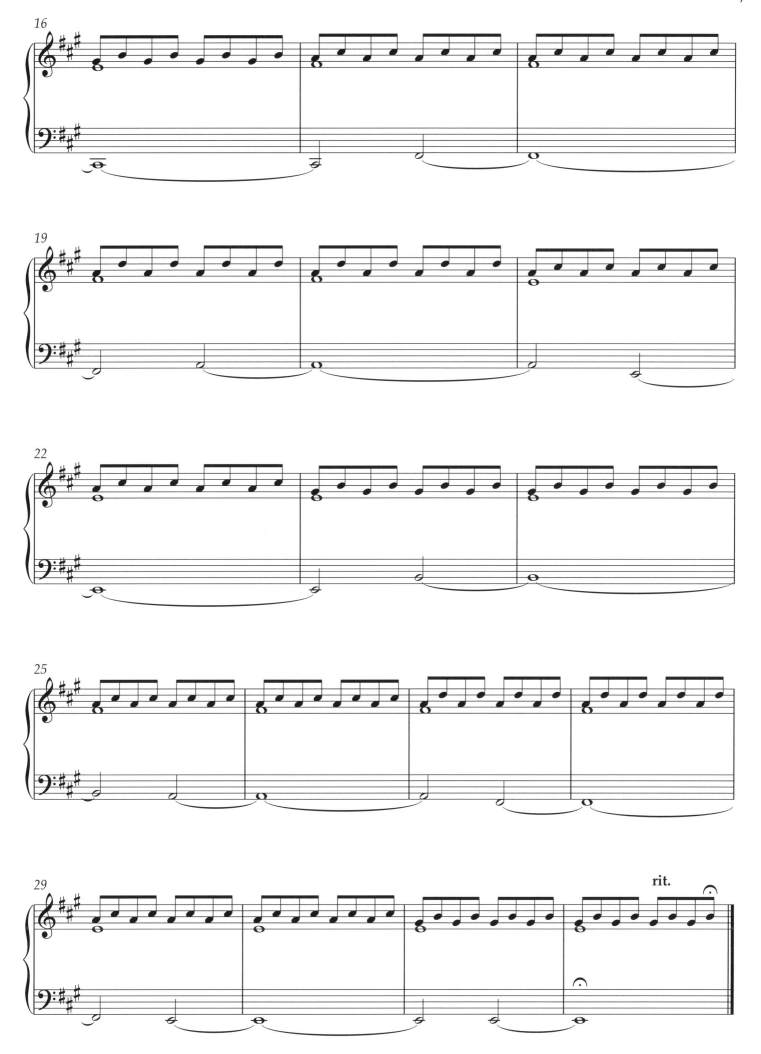

Pavane pour une infante défunte

Maurice Ravel

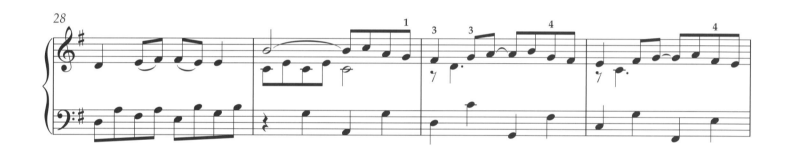

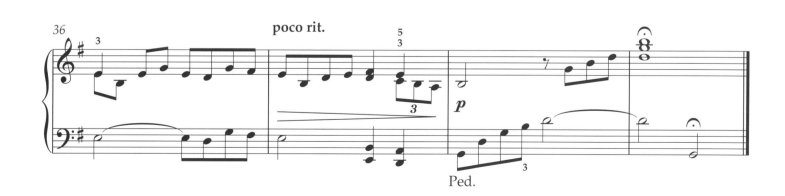

Piano Concerto No.21
Second movement

Wolfgang Amadeus Mozart

Piano Sonata No.14 'Moonlight'

Ludwig van Beethoven

Ashokan Farewell

Jay Ungar

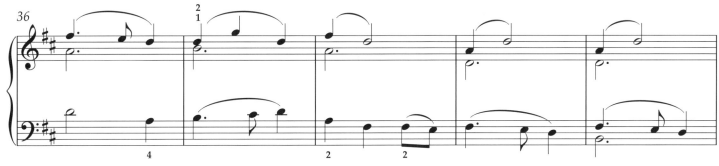

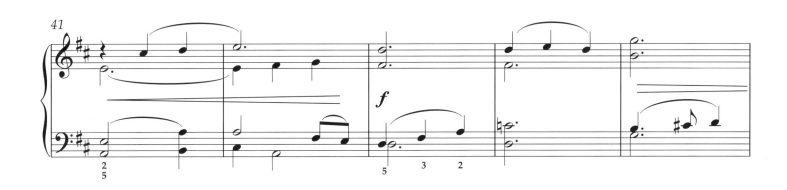

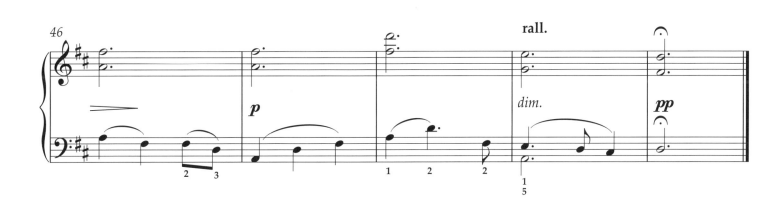

Gnossienne No.1

Erik Satie

Clair de lune

Claude Debussy

Prelude No.15 'Raindrop'

Frédéric Chopin

Piano Concerto No.20
Second movement

Wolfgang Amadeus Mozart

Liebestraum No.3

Poco allegro, con affetto ♩. = 48

Franz Liszt

rall.

War Song

Phamie Gow

Concerto for Piano and Orchestra

Second movement theme

Nigel Hess

The Girl with the Flaxen Hair

Claude Debussy

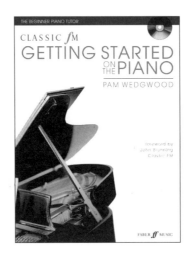

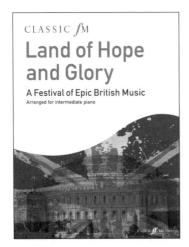